Standard Grade

MATHS
REVISION NOTES

Morvyth Davis

Published by   Leckie & Leckie
         8 Whitehill Terrace
         St Andrews KY16 8RN
         Tel 0334 - 75656

A CIP Catalogue record for this book
is available from the British Library.
ISBN 0-9515718-5-0

Leckie & Leckie

CONTENTS

Note:

At the beginning of each chapter is a list of the topics dealt with in that chapter, stating for which level each topic is appropriate.

    G — General paper
    C — Early part of Credit paper
    C* — More difficult parts of Credit paper

INTRODUCTION

HOW TO USE THIS BOOK

These revision notes sum up the main points from the Standard Grade course, at General and Credit levels. Each topic in the contents list at the beginning of each Chapter is coded 'G' for the General course, 'C' for the Credit course. (C* denotes particularly demanding Credit work.)

Students following a General course and who do not plan to sit the Credit papers should do only the topics coded 'G'.

Credit/General, (students concentrating on General but who have done some Credit work as well), should cover the 'G' and 'C' topics.

Students following a full Credit course should cover all the material in these notes.

Important facts and formulas you must know have been highlighted, and there are hints throughout the book on answering exam questions.

Spend some of your revision time working on examples.

AND WHEN YOU GET TO THE EXAM!

Be sure to write down all your working. The examiner can only judge your work by what you write down, so let him or her see what you are thinking.

Read the questions carefully. The second paper will have some longer questions split into several parts. If you race too quickly through the easy part at the beginning and don't quite get the idea of what you are really being asked to do, then you may be throwing away marks.

YOU AND YOUR CALCULATOR

Standard Grade Maths assumes you have a Scientific calculator and you will be at a great disadvantage if you haven't. Make sure you have your own calculator and that you know how to operate it. Borrowing someone else's for the exam is just not the same since each type of calculator has slight differences.

In this book there are calculator hints to help you avoid some common mistakes. Most importantly, remember to check that the answers you get with your calculator are sensible!

CHAPTER 1—FORMULAE AND EQUATIONS

CONTENTS

MAKING AND USING FORMULAE

Look at these patterns of black and white tiles:

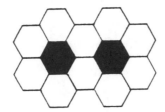

What is the formula linking the number of black and the number of white tiles?

Make a table:

black b	1	2	3	4	5	etc
white w	6	10	14	18	22	etc

Perhaps you can see the formula right away. If not, notice that the values of w go up in 4's, so the formula will have '4b' in it. Work out the values for 4b:

4b	4	8	12	16	etc

Now we see that w is always 2 more than 4b.

Formula:

$$w = 4b + 2$$

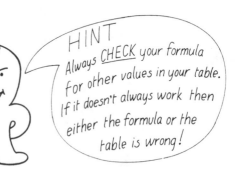

HINT
Always <u>CHECK</u> your formula for other values in your table. If it doesn't always work then either the formula or the table is wrong!

Here is an example of substitution into a formula:

The formula for the height of a stone t seconds after it is thrown vertically upwards is:

$$h = ut - 5t^2$$

where u is the speed at which the stone is thrown.

A stone is thrown at a speed of 30 m/s. What is its height after 2 seconds?

Substituting t=2 and u=30 into the formula gives:

$$h = 30 \times 2 - 5 \times 2^2$$
$$= 60 - 20$$
$$= 40$$

The height is 40 metres.

EQUATIONS AND INEQUATIONS

Example 1

$3x+9 = x+5$ Find x.

	$3x+9 = x+5$
Take x from both sides:	$2x+9 = 5$
Take 9 from both sides:	$2x = -4$
Divide both sides by 2:	$\mathbf{x = -2}$

Example 2

Solve $3n>7$, where n is a whole number.

	$3n>7$
Divide by 3:	$n>2.33$

So since n is a whole number, **n is 3, 4, 5, etc.**

MORE DIFFICULT EQUATIONS AND INEQUATIONS

Example 1

Jane's backpack weighed twice as much as Anne's, but by transferring 1 kg of her load to Anne's pack, Anne had two-thirds as much weight as Jane. What weight was each girl carrying at the start?

Let x stand for Anne's load at the start, so Jane's is 2x.

After the transfer: Anne has $x+1$

Jane has $2x-1$

so:	$x+1=\frac{2}{3}(2x-1)$
multiply by 3 to remove fractions:	$3x+3=2(2x-1)$
which gives:	$x=5$ (you can check this)

So to begin with **Anne's pack weighed 5 kg and Jane's 10 kg.**

Example 2

Solve: $\dfrac{2x+1}{4} - \dfrac{2x-1}{3} \leqslant \dfrac{5}{6}$

Multiply by 12:

$$3(2x+1) - 4(2x-1) \leqslant 10$$
$$6x+3 - 8x+4 \leqslant 10$$
$$-2x \leqslant 3$$

Must remember. If I multiply or divide an inequality by something negative, I must change round the inequality sign.

so if
$$-2x \leqslant 3$$
$$2x \geqslant -3$$
$$\mathbf{x \geqslant -1{\cdot}5}$$

PROVING/DISPROVING A CONJECTURE

Look again at the formula on page 3 for the design of black and white tiles.

We can **check** that w = 4b+2 for particular values of b.

Can we **prove** that w = 4b+2 for **all** values of b?

Here is one of the patterns divided up into several sections:—

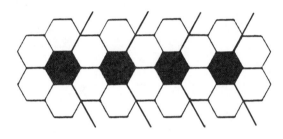

And then pulled apart:—

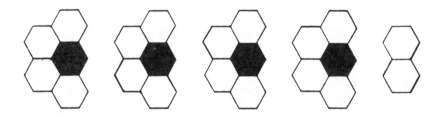

Each section has 1 black tile and 4 white tiles. 2 extra white are needed at the end.

We can see that however many sections the pattern has, this will always be true.

So the number of white tiles will be four times the number of black tiles, plus two.

That is w = 4b + 2.

If a conjecture is **not true,** it can be disproved by finding just one counter example:—

Conjecture: If n is an integer, n^2 is odd.

We can take $n = 2$ to give a counter example.

If $n = 2$, then $n^2 = 4$, and n^2 is not odd.

Since we have found a counter example, we have shown that the conjecture is false.

6

MORE ABOUT FORMULAE

Example 1

The formula for the volume of a cone is:

$$V = \tfrac{1}{3}\pi r^2 h$$

Change the subject of this formula to r, and then find the radius of a cone which has a height of 10 cm and holds 1 litre.

Multiply by 3: $\qquad 3V = \pi r^2 h$

Change sides over: $\quad \pi r^2 h = 3V$

Divide by πh: $\qquad r^2 = \dfrac{3V}{\pi h}$

$$r = \pm\sqrt{\dfrac{3V}{\pi h}}$$

Substitute values: $\qquad r = +\sqrt{\dfrac{3\times 1000}{3\cdot 14\times 10}}$ $\qquad$ (we only consider the +ve root since radius must be positive)

$$= \sqrt{95\cdot 54}$$

radius is 9·8 cm

(to 1 decimal place)

Don't forget to say WHY you are rejecting one possible answer

Example 2

What would the effect on the volume of a cone be if the radius of the base were increased by 20% but the height remained unchanged?

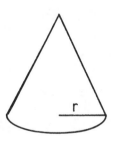

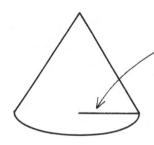

r + 20% of r, that is, 120% of r, which is $\dfrac{120}{100}$ r

$V_1 = \tfrac{1}{3}\pi r^2 h$

$V_2 = \tfrac{1}{3}\pi\left(\dfrac{120}{100}r\right)^2 h$

$\quad = \dfrac{14\,400}{10\,000}\times \tfrac{1}{3}\pi r^2 h$

$\quad = \dfrac{144}{100}\times V_1$

So the **volume is multiplied by a factor of 1·44.**

If you find this very difficult, you could choose numbers for r and h and work it out that way.

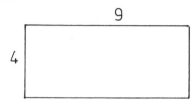

With a quadratic equation, expect to get TWO solutions, although they might both be the same.

Example 1

Solve: $x^2-9x=0$.

Take out common factor: $x(x-9)=0$

So **$x=0$ or $x=9$.**

Example 2

9

4

When all the sides of the rectangle opposite are increased by the same amount the area is 73 square units.

Find this increase, correct to one decimal place.

Let x be the increase, so for the new rectangle—length $=9+x$
breadth$=4+x$

So Area$=(9+x)(4+x)=73$
$36+13x+x^2=73$
$x^2+13x-37=0$

this is standard quadratic form—always arrange terms in this order.

If a quadratic equation will factorise then that will be the quickest way to solve it — but this equation doesn't factorise, so we must use the quadratic formula.

The quadratic formula: $x = \dfrac{-b \pm \sqrt{b^2-4ac}}{2a}$ **LEARN!**

For the equation above, a=1, b=13, c=-37

Substituting:
$$x = \frac{-13 \pm \sqrt{169+148}}{2}$$
$$= \frac{-13 \pm 17 \cdot 80}{2}$$
$$= 2 \cdot 4 \text{ or } -15 \cdot 4$$

but a negative answer would not make sense for an increase — look at the diagram.

If you reject one of the solutions, always remember to say why.

So the increase is 2·4 units, to 1 decimal place.

CHAPTER 2—SHAPE

CONTENTS

MEASUREMENT

The metric system is based on the metre (length), litre (volume), and gram (mass or 'weight').

You must know these facts:

Length	Area	Mass	Volume
10 mm=1 cm	10 000 m²=1 hectare	1000 g=1 kg	1000 ml=1 litre
100 cm=1 m		1000 kg=1 tonne	1000 cm³=1 litre
1000 m=1 km			

ANGLE

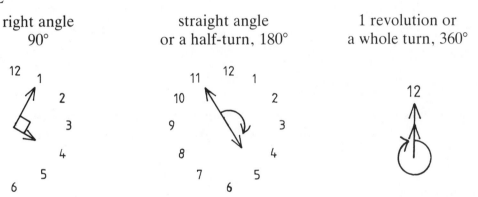

| right angle 90° | straight angle or a half-turn, 180° | 1 revolution or a whole turn, 360° |

In the following diagrams the angles have been marked to show which are equal.

X shape   **Z shape**   **F shape**

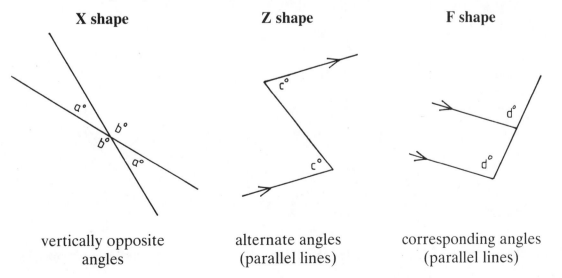

vertically opposite angles · alternate angles (parallel lines) · corresponding angles (parallel lines)

Angle sum in a triangle

Angle sum in a polygon:
Divide it into triangles, and count
multiples of 180°

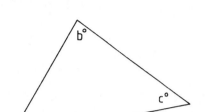

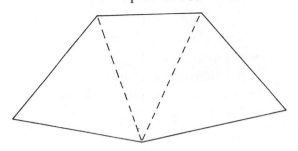

a+b+c=180
for every triangle

There are 3 triangles, so 3×180°
giving a total of 540°

SYMMETRY

Bilateral symmetry

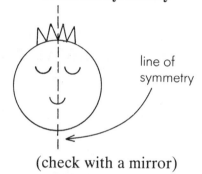

line of symmetry

(check with a mirror)

Rotational symmetry

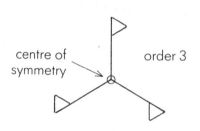

centre of symmetry   order 3

(Check with tracing paper—
pivot the paper around the centre)

TWO DIMENSIONAL SHAPES

If we know what lines of symmetry a shape has, and whether it has rotational symmetry, we can work out the properties of its sides, angles and diagonals.

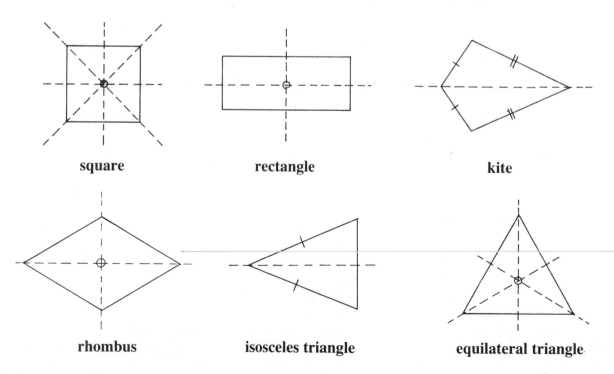

square   **rectangle**   **kite**

rhombus   **isosceles triangle**   **equilateral triangle**

The parallelogram has no lines of symmetry but does have half-turn symmetry.

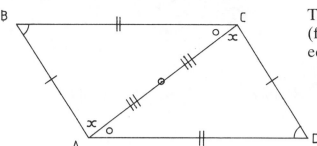

Triangle ABC is congruent to CDA (fits exactly on top) so we can pick out equal sides and angles.

AREA OF TWO DIMENSIONAL SHAPES

We need two formulae:

Area of rectangle=length×breadth
Area of triangle=½(base×height)

Example

The picture shows the front view of a greenhouse. It is all glass except for the door. Find the area of glass required for the front.

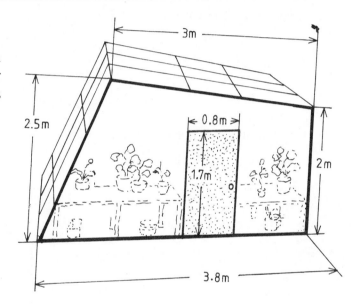

All straight-edged shapes can be divided up into triangles and rectangles, so we can find the area of any straight-edged shape.

Draw a plan and divide it up.

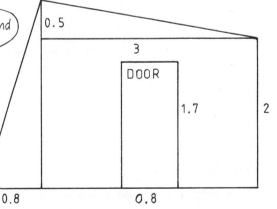

Find the total area of the front:

top triangle:	½×(0·5×3)=0·75
side triangle:	½×(0·8×2·5)=1
large rectangle:	3×2=6
total:	7·75 m²
Take away area of door:	1·7×0·8=1·36 m²
so	**area of glass=6·39m².**

THREE DIMENSIONAL SHAPES

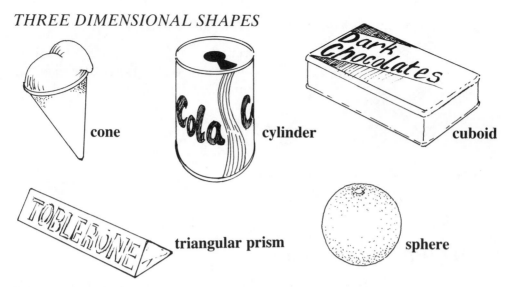

cone   cylinder   cuboid

triangular prism   sphere

When a model of a solid is made from straws and pipecleaners it is easy to see its **edges** (the straws) and its **vertices** or corners (where the pipecleaners go).

square-based pyramid:

5 vertices

8 edges.

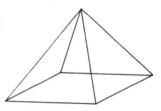

When a model is constructed from a net drawn on card then its **faces** are easily seen:

net of a cuboid:

6 faces, all rectangular.

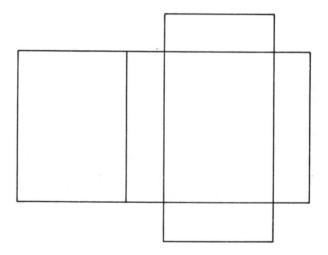

TOLERANCE

Measurements are never completely accurate. If a large number of 30 mm screws were examined under a microscope we would find some a bit longer than 30 mm, and some shorter.

If the manufacturer claimed they all measured 30 mm, ±0·2 mm, what would be the greatest and least length allowed?

30 mm+0·2 mm = **30·2 mm greatest.**

30 mm−0·2 mm = **29·8 mm least.**

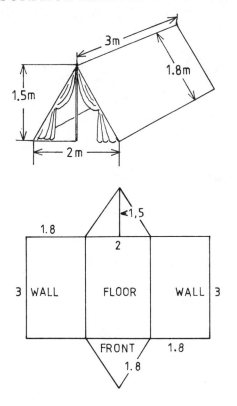

What area of canvas is needed to make this tent, which has a canvas floor section too?

Drawing a net helps here, and write the dimensions in to help you.

area of floor=3×2=6
area of wall=3×1·8=5·4
area of front=½×2×1·5=1·5

total area (floor, two walls, front and back)=**19·8 square metres.**

Prisms have the same cross-section all the way up.

Here are some prisms, along with their names and, in brackets, the shape of their cross-sections.

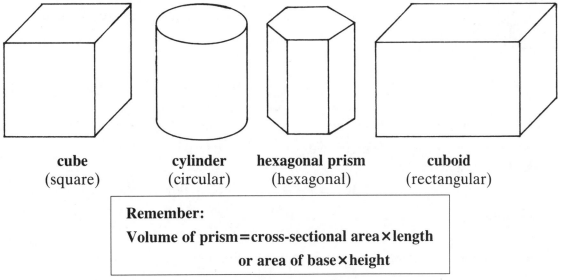

cube
(square)

cylinder
(circular)

hexagonal prism
(hexagonal)

cuboid
(rectangular)

> **Remember:**
> **Volume of prism=cross-sectional area×length**
> **or area of base×height**

The tent in the previous example is a triangular prism, but you might need to imagine it standing on its end to see this.

Let's now find its volume:

Cross-sectional area=1·5 m² (this is the front or back)
    Length=3 m
    So Volume=1.5×3=**4·5 cubic metres.**

> **Area/volume—remember square/cubic units!**

MORE ON SURFACE AREA AND VOLUME

This tank is a cylinder with hemispherical ends. Its diameter is 3 metres and it holds 57 500 litres.

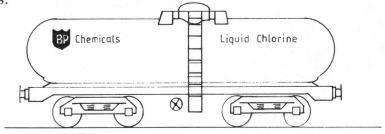

Volume of sphere$=\frac{4}{3}\pi r^3$ Surface area of sphere$=4\pi r^2$

(a) What is its total length?

The two curved end sections together make a sphere of radius 1·5 m.
Volume of hemispherical ends$=\frac{4}{3}\times\pi\times1\cdot5^3=14\cdot13$ m^3
but total volume$=57500$ litres$=57\cdot5$ m^3
so volume of cylindrical section$=57\cdot5-14\cdot13=43\cdot37$ m^3
but volume of cylinder$=\pi r^2h=3\cdot14\times1\cdot5^2\times h$
so $3\cdot14\times1\cdot5^2\times h=43\cdot37$
and $h=\dfrac{43\cdot37}{3\cdot14\times1\cdot5^2}=\textbf{6·1 m.}$

Remember 43·37 is to be **divided** by 3·14 and **divided** by 1·5^2, that is, $43\cdot37\div(3\cdot14\times1\cdot5^2)$

This key sequence will give you the **wrong answer:**
$43\cdot37\div3\cdot14\times1\cdot5^2$.

Make sure **now** that you can find a correct key sequence.

Total length of tank is $6\cdot1+(2\times1\cdot5)=\textbf{9·1 metres}$ (to 2 significant figures).

(b) Find the surface area of the tank.

The surface area is made up of two parts—the surface of a sphere, and the curved surface of a cylinder.

Sphere: Area$=4\pi r^2=4\times3\cdot14\times1\cdot5^2=28\cdot26$m^2
Cylinder: length is 6·1 m, breadth is $2\pi r$ which is $2\times3\cdot14\times1\cdot5$
                area$=6\cdot1\times2\times3\cdot14\times1\cdot5=57\cdot462$ m^2

Total surface area$=$85·7 m^2 (to 3 significant figures).

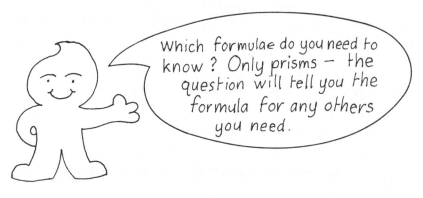

Which formulae do you need to know? Only prisms — the question will tell you the formula for any others you need.

CHAPTER 3—SOME ARITHMETIC

CONTENTS

STANDARD FORM (SCIENTIFIC NOTATION)

> $a \times 10^n$ a must be between 1 and 10.
>
> n is positive for large numbers and negative for small numbers.

Large numbers: $139\,000\,000\,000$ is written as $1 \cdot 39 \times 10^{11}$

3×10^6 is the number $3\,000\,000$.

Small numbers: $0 \cdot 00000026$ will be $2 \cdot 6 \times 10^{-7}$

$3 \cdot 576 \times 10^{-1}$ is the number $0 \cdot 3576$.

Remember!
$10^1 = 10$
and $10^0 = 1$

PERCENTAGE DISCOUNT

What is the reduction on the soup, expressed as a percentage of the original price?

Reduction = 8p

Percentage Discount $= \dfrac{8}{49} \times 100$

$= \mathbf{16 \cdot 3\%}$.

INSURANCE PREMIUMS

Example 1

Use the table below to find the cost of holiday insurance for 2 people going on a fortnight's package holiday to Spain.

Period	Europe	USA	Outwith Europe/USA
up to 9 days	£13·90	£18·60	£19·40
up to 17 days	£14·90	£20·80	£21·40
up to 31 days	£17·90	£24·80	£25·00

A fortnight is 2 weeks, that is 14 days, so we look in row for 'up to 17 days', and as Spain is in Europe we look at the Europe column.

The premium is £14·90 per person, so 2 people will pay a total of **£29·80**.

Example 2

The contents of Lorna's flat are worth £12 000 and she wants to insure them with a company whose premium is £0·45 per £100 insured. She is entitled to a 7·5% discount because she has good quality locks on her door and is a member of a Neighbourhood Watch Scheme.

Find her annual premium.

£12 000 is 120 times £100, so basic premium is £0·45×120=£54
Discount=7·5% of £54=£4·05.   Subtract this from £54.

Her annual premium will be **£49·95**.

TIME, DISTANCE AND SPEED

Example 1

Khalid wants to find the total time for his 3 trials in the 1500 m event. His times are 4:53, 5:08 and 4:48. (4:53 means 4 minutes and 53 seconds).

Seconds: 53+8+48 gives 109 seconds.
As there are 60 seconds in a minute, this is 1 minute and 49 seconds.

Minutes: 4+5+4=13.
The total time is 13 minutes+1 minute 49 seconds, which is:

14 minutes 49 seconds.

Example 2

(a) Lesley left Inverness at 0945 and arrived in Edinburgh at 1420. How long did she spend travelling?

0945—1000 is 15 minutes
1000—1400 is 4 hours
1400—1420 is 20 minutes

Altogether this is **4 hours 35 minutes**.

(b) The distance from Inverness to Edinburgh is 158 miles. Work out the average speed for Lesley's journey in miles per hour, to one decimal place.

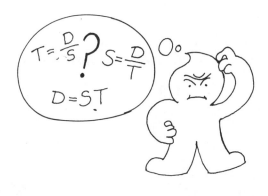

We use $S = \dfrac{D}{T}$.   D=158 miles.

T = 4 hours 35 minutes

$= 4\dfrac{35}{60}$ hours=4·583 hours

$S = \dfrac{D}{T} = \dfrac{158 \text{ miles}}{4\cdot583 \text{ hours}} = 34\cdot47$ mph

Lesley's average speed was **34·5 miles per hour**, to one decimal place.

SIMPLE INTEREST

Example

Neil deposits £300 in a Building Society account which pays 6% interest per annum. What interest will he gain after 2 months?

Interest for 1 year = 6% of £300 = **£18**   Interest for 2 months = $\frac{2}{12}$ of £18 = **£3**

COMPOUND INTEREST AND DEPRECIATION

Example

(a) Fiona buys a second-hand car for £4,300. It is depreciating at a rate of 20% each year. What will it be worth after she has had it for 2 years?

Value at start   = £4300
1st year depreciation   = 20% of £4300 = £860
Value after 1 year   = £(4300−860) = £3440
2nd year depreciation = 20% of £3440 = £688
Value after 2 years   = £(3440−688) = £2752

After 2 years Fiona's car is worth about **£2750**.

Value at start   = £4300
Value after 1 year   = 80% of £4300 = 0·8×£4300
Value after 2 years   = 80% of value after 1 year
                       = 0·8×(0·8×£4300) = $(0·8)^2$×£4300 = **£2752**

(b) Fiona buys a car for £A, and it depreciates at a rate of 30% per annum. Show that it will be worth £$(0·7)^2$A after 2 years, and write down an expression for its value after 4 years.

Value at start   = £A
Value after 1 year   = 70% of £A = £(0·7)A
Value after 2 years   = 70% of £0·7A = 0·7×0·7A = £$(0·7)^2$A

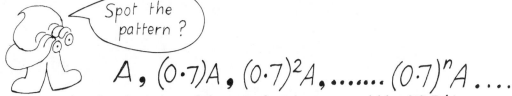

$$A, \ (0·7)A, \ (0·7)^2A, \ldots\ldots\ldots (0·7)^nA \ldots$$

An expression for the value of the car after 4 years would be **£$(0·7)^4$A**.

17

CHAPTER 4—GRAPHS AND FUNCTIONS

CONTENTS

GRAPHS AS PICTURES

If you have ever filled a milk bottle from a tap you'll know how the water level rises slowly for a while then suddenly rises quickly when you get to the narrow neck.

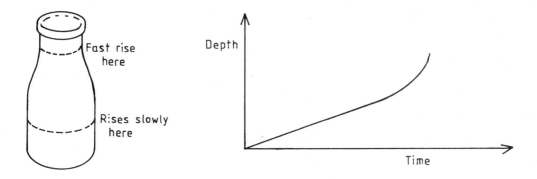

Here is a drawing of a roller coaster. Below it a graph has been drawn to show how the speed varies as you go from the start to the half-way point.

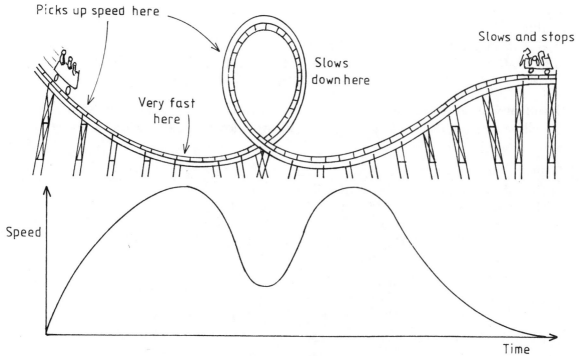

STRAIGHT LINE GRAPHS

Example

Fit'n'Firm Health Club charges £5 a visit. BodyGlow Health Club charges a membership fee of £20 plus £2 a visit. Show on a graph the cost of each Club for different numbers of visits and say which Club is the cheaper.

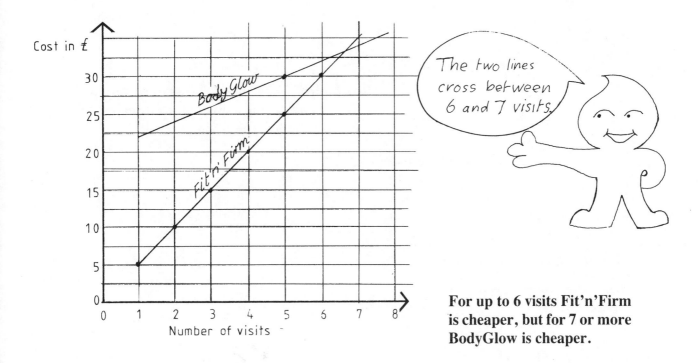

For up to 6 visits Fit'n'Firm is cheaper, but for 7 or more BodyGlow is cheaper.

LINEAR FUNCTION AND GRAPH

> **Remember:**
>
> **y=mx+c.   This is the equation of a straight line with gradient m which cuts the y-axis at (0,c).**

An equation may need to be rearranged before you can tell its gradient and y-intercept.

Example

What is the gradient and y-intercept of the line 3x+2y=8?

$3x+2y=8$
$\quad 2y=-3x+8$
$\quad\ \ y=-\tfrac{3}{2}x+4$

compare with y=mx+c

so **gradient is $-\tfrac{3}{2}$,**

y-intercept is 4.

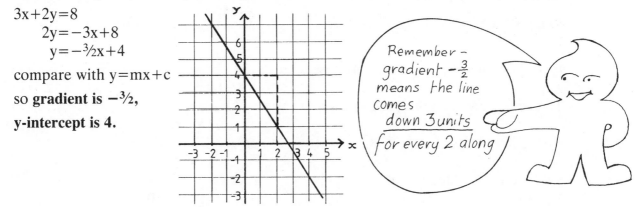

QUADRATIC FUNCTION

> **Remember:**
>
> $f(x) = ax^2 + bx + c$ where a, b and c are constants, is the equation of a quadratic function and its graph is a parabola.

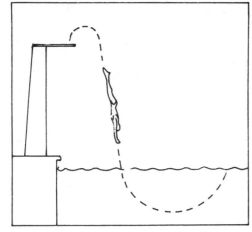

This graph $h(t) = t^2 - 8t + 7$ shows the position of a diver's head during a dive, plotted against the time since she left the diving board.

When did she resurface?

How long was she underwater?

What was the lowest depth she reached?

When she hits the water and when she resurfaces $h(t) = 0$!

so $t^2 - 8t + 7 = 0$
$(t-1)(t-7) = 0$ (by factorising the quadratic)
so $t = 1$ or $t = 7$

This means the diver hit the water after 1 second, and resurfaced after 7 seconds. She was underwater for 6 seconds.

The graph is symmetrical, so she reached the lowest depth halfway between 1 second and 7 seconds, that means after 4 seconds so find h when $t = 4$

when $t = 4$,
$h(t) = 16 - 32 + 7$
$= -9$

So she dived to a depth of 9 feet.

SIMULTANEOUS EQUATIONS

Example 1

Find the point of intersection of these 2 lines:

$$3x - 2y = 8 \quad \dots \dots \dots \dots \quad (1)$$
$$5x + 8y = 70 \quad \dots \dots \dots \dots \quad (2)$$

To eliminate y, we multiply equation (1) by 4:

$$12x - 8y = 32 \quad \dots \dots \dots \dots \quad (1)$$
$$5x + 8y = 70 \quad \dots \dots \dots \dots \quad (2)$$

Now add: $\qquad\qquad 17x = 102$

Solve for x: $\qquad\qquad\quad x = 6$

Substitute this value into equation (1): $\quad 3 \times 6 - 2y = 8$

Solve for y: $\qquad\qquad\qquad -2y = -10$
$$y = 5$$

The point of intersection is (6, 5).

Example 2   One linear and one quadratic equation

In an 'It's a Knock-Out' competition, contestants had to shoot arrows from the top of a tower.

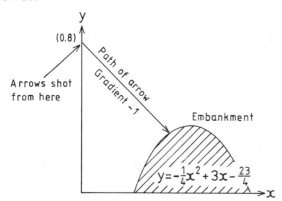

A cross-sectional diagram has been drawn on a coordinate grid to show path of arrow.

To find this contestant's arrow, we work out where the straight line and the curve intersect.

Line through (0, 8) with gradient -1, is $y=8-x$

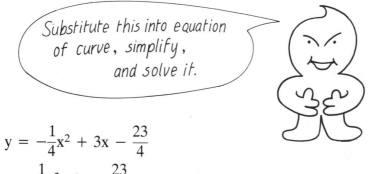

$$y = -\frac{1}{4}x^2 + 3x - \frac{23}{4}$$

becomes $8-x=-\frac{1}{4}x^2+3x - \frac{23}{4}$

which is $x^2-16x+55=0$ after simplifying.   (Check for yourself.)
Solutions $x=5$ or $x=11$.

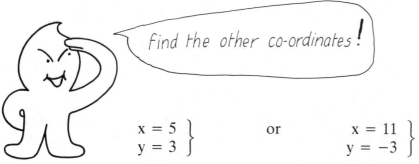

$$\left. \begin{array}{l} x = 5 \\ y = 3 \end{array} \right\} \qquad \text{or} \qquad \left. \begin{array}{l} x = 11 \\ y = -3 \end{array} \right\}$$

Looking again at the sketch we can tell that (5, 3) is the correct answer and (11, −3) should be rejected.

The arrow will be found at (5, 3).

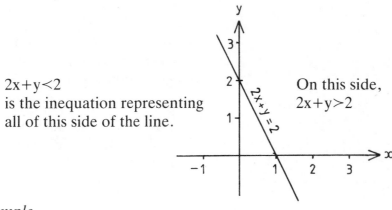

2x+y<2
is the inequation representing
all of this side of the line.

On this side,
2x+y>2

Example

(a) Cement is made by mixing x parts of concrete with y parts of sand. The shaded area on the graph below shows the possible values of x and y under certain restrictions. What are these restrictions?

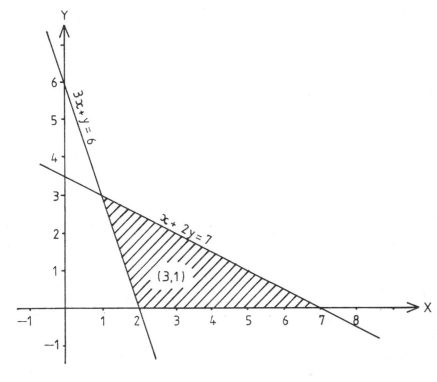

We can see that x and y cannot be negative, so x⩾0 and y⩾0.

The area is also bounded by two lines: x+2y=7 and 3x+y=6.

We must decide which of these is correct: x+2y>7 or x+2y<7.
and which of these: 3x+y>6 or 3x+y<6.

Choose any point in the shaded area, for example (3, 1).

For (3, 1), x+2y=3+2=5, so x+2y<7.

Doing the same for (3, 1) and the other line we find 3x+y>6.

The restrictions on x and y are: x⩾0, y⩾0, x+2y⩽7 and 3x+y⩾6.

(b) If concrete costs £4 per part and sand £1 per part, and the restrictions above apply, what quantities of concrete and sand should be used to minimise the cost?

Cost = x parts at £4 + y parts at £1 = £(4x + y)

The highest (maximum) and lowest (minimum) values will always occur around the edges of the region, so we investigate each of the vertices:

At (2, 0)   4x+y=8+0=8
At (1, 3)   4x+y=4+3=7   ← this is the lowest cost
At (7, 0)   4x+y=28+0=28

So the minimum cost is when **1 part of concrete is mixed with 3 parts sand.**

22

GRAPH OF $y=a^x$

A smart 12-year-old made a deal with her parents regarding pocket money. 'I know you're hard-up, Dad, so I'll take a reduction in pocket money this year—just give me £1 a week—on condition that you give me double that next year and double again the next and so on, so that I get a bit more as I get older to take account of inflation.'

'Seems very fair,' said Mum, and Dad agreed.

Well, she was 18 when she left school and her parents had long since regretted the deal. Why?

Let's work it out—

Her pocket money amount would increase like this:

£1, £2, £4, £8, £16, £32, £64, . . .

By the age of 18 she would be receiving £64 pocket money per week.

The amounts could be expressed as powers of 2:

$1=2^0$, $2=2^1$, $4=2^2$, $8=2^3$, etc.

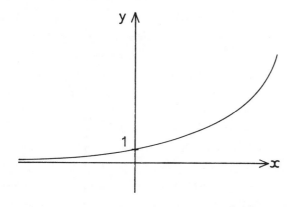

This is the graph of $y=2^x$

It shows rapid growth.

Some negative values for x have also been taken.

The function $y=a^x$ is called the exponential function, and each graph passes through the point (0, 1).

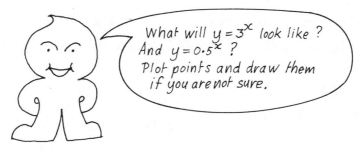

What will $y=3^x$ look like?
And $y=0.5^x$?
Plot points and draw them if you are not sure.

FAMILIES OF CURVES

When the curve $y=x^2$ is moved parallel to the x-axis you can write down the new equation:

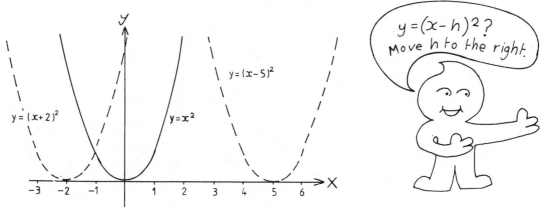

$y=(x-h)^2$?
Move h to the right.

23

Some more images of $y=x^2$ have been shown with dotted lines:

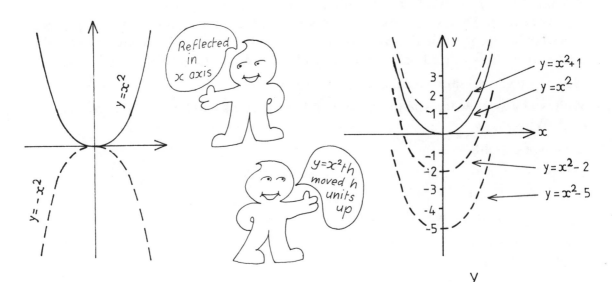

Example 1

In the diagram opposite, the graph of $y=x^2$ has been moved to the position shown. What is the equation of this parabola?

The curve has been moved 2 units to the left and 1 up, so:

$y=(x+2)^2+1$ or $y=x^2+4x+5$

Example 2

What will $y=x^2-6x+7$ look like?

$$y=x^2-6x+9-2$$
$$y=(x-3)^2-2 \qquad \text{(method of completing the square)}$$

So the graph will be the curve $y=x^2$ moved 3 units to the right and 2 down.

GRAPHICAL SOLUTIONS

Here is the graph of $y=x^3-3x$

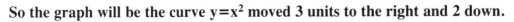

Example 1

Use the graph to find solutions for $x^3-3x=-x$.

This is the same as solving $y=x^3-3x$
$\qquad\qquad$ and $y=-x$ $\qquad$ simultaneously.

Draw in the line $y=-x$ on the graph and read off the intersections.

You should get: **$x=0$, $x=1\cdot4$ and $x=-1\cdot4$.**

Example 2

For what values of k will $x^3-3x=k$ have 3 solutions?

$\qquad$ This is like solving $y=x^3-3x$
$\qquad\qquad$ and $y=k$ $\qquad$ simultaneously.

Lines with equation $y=k$ are horizontal lines.

If $k>2$ or $k<-2$ then a horizontal line will cut the graph only once.

If **$-2<x<2$** then the horizontal line will cut the curve 3 times.

ITERATION

Example

The equation $x^3-3x=0$ has 3 solutions, as we can see from the last graph on previous page. One of them is 0. Another lies between $1\cdot5$ and 2. Use an iterative method to find this root correct to 2 decimal places.

$f(x)=x^3-3x$ and $f(1\cdot5)<0$ and $f(2)>0$

We must narrow down the interval between $1\cdot5$ and 2 until we find more precisely where the curve cuts the x-axis. Each time we try the mid-point of the interval.

Put results in table:

root lies between:	
1·5	2

Try $\dfrac{1\cdot5+2}{2}=1\cdot75$

(1·75 is the mid point of the interval from 1·5 to 2.)

$f(1\cdot75)=0\cdot109>0$ $\qquad$ enter:

1·5	1·75

Try $\dfrac{1\cdot5+1\cdot75}{2}=1\cdot625$

$f(1\cdot625)=-0\cdot583<0$ $\qquad$ enter:

1·625	1·75
1·687	1·75

If we continue in this way, we will get the values in the table opposite. (Check for yourself)

1·718	1·75
1·718	1·734
1·726	1·734

We do not need to go any further, since both numbers are 1·73 correct to 2 decimal places. **The root is approximately 1·73**, and by symmetry the third root is $-1\cdot73$.

CHAPTER 5—MAPS, PLANS AND SIMILAR SHAPES

CONTENTS

SIMILAR SHAPES

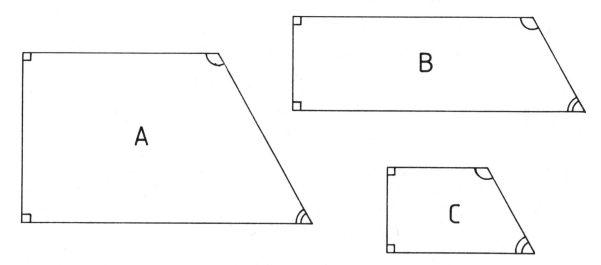

The shapes above are equiangular—they all have the same sizes of angles. The equal angles have been marked on the shapes.

We can see that A and C are similar in shape, but B is not similar to A or C—it is too long compared to its breadth.

Measure the sides of A and C.

You will find that—A is an enlargement of C with scale factor 2,

      or   C is a reduction of A, scale factor ½.

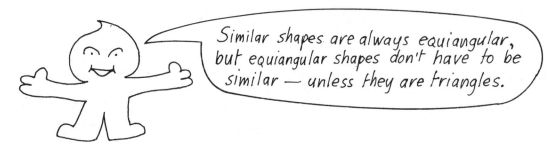

Similar shapes are always equiangular, but equiangular shapes don't have to be similar — unless they are triangles.

MAPS—SCALE

A map is an example of a reduction—a reduction of the real world. A map must give the scale to which it is drawn. For example, scale 1:50000 means the real lengths are 50000 times longer than on the map.

      1 cm   stands for   50000 cm=500 m

   on the map   on the ground.

Example

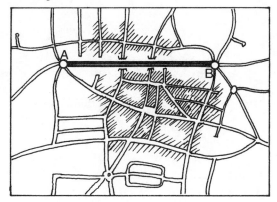

The motorway is 96 km long.
(AB on the map).

What is the scale of this map?

4 cm	represents	96 km
1 cm		24 km
		= 24 000 m
		= 2 400 000 cm

So scale of map is 1 : 2 400 000.

MAPS—DIRECTION

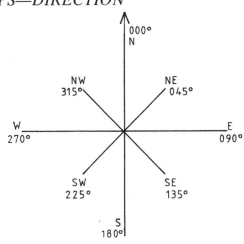

Diagram showing compass points and three-figure bearings.

Example

The bearing of **B from A** is 075°.

What is the bearing of **A from B?**

By drawing the North line at B, and marking a pair of alternate angles made by parallel lines, we can calculate the size of the angle marked with the arrow as 180°+75°, which is 255°. **The bearing of A from B is 255°.**

Since all North lines are parallel, look for alternate and corresponding angles.

SIMILAR TRIANGLES

Example

From the point marked A, the
tops of the 2 mountains
are in line with
each other.

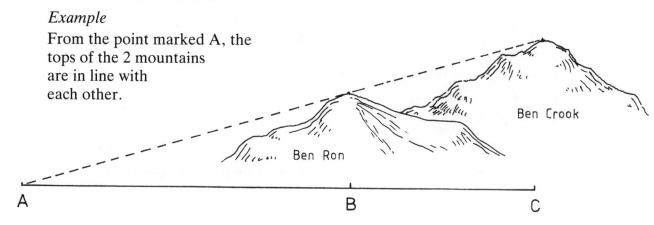

Ben Ron is 1 931 feet high and Ben Crook 2 557 feet high. The distance from A to B is 7·8 miles. How far is it from A to C?

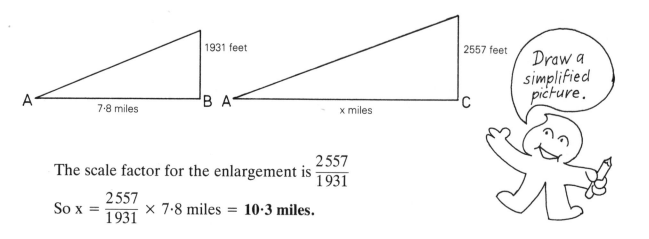

The scale factor for the enlargement is $\dfrac{2557}{1931}$

So x $= \dfrac{2557}{1931} \times 7{\cdot}8$ miles $=$ **10·3 miles.**

SKETCHES VERSUS SCALE DRAWINGS

A sketch is a rough picture, usually drawn to help you decide what calculations you need to make to solve a problem.

A scale drawing must be accurate, with angles and lines all drawn to the correct measurements.

If an examination question says something like, 'answers obtained from scale drawings will receive no credit' then it is your knowledge of algebra and trigonometry which is being tested, and any diagrams you draw are only to help you understand the question.

If a scale drawing is required you must use the appropriate mathematical instruments as accurately as possible.

Hints for diagrams:

1. **Use a pencil, not pen.**
2. **Write in lengths and angle sizes as you go along.**
3. **If you are drawing North lines, make sure they are all parallel.**
4. **If a scale is given, or even suggested, then use it.**
5. **If you are choosing the scale yourself make sure the diagram is clear and not too small.**
6. **Don't start too near the edge of the page.**

AREA OF SIMILAR SHAPES

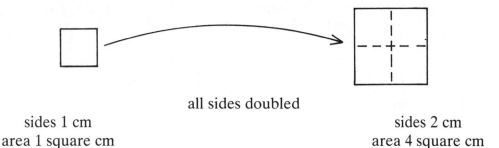

all sides doubled

sides 1 cm
area 1 square cm

sides 2 cm
area 4 square cm

The lengths are in the ratio $1:2$.
So areas are in the ratio $1:4$ (which is $1^2:2^2$).

Example

A large photograph of area 108 cm² is to be reduced, using scale factor ⅓, to give a passport size photograph. What will be the area of the passport photograph?

Scale factor ⅓ means lengths are in ratio $1:3$

So areas are in ratio $1^2:3^2=1:9$

So the passport photograph's area will be ⅑ of 108 cm², which is **12 cm².**

MORE ON SIMILAR TRIANGLES

Are these triangles similar?

If they are, then the 3 ratios formed by taking corresponding sides will be equal.

Ratio of shortest sides $=\dfrac{7\cdot1}{5\cdot1}=1\cdot4$ (to 2 significant figures)

Ratio of longest sides $=\dfrac{15\cdot1}{10\cdot8}=1\cdot4$

Ratio of remaining sides $=\dfrac{8\cdot7}{6\cdot2}=1\cdot4$

Since they are all equal, **the triangles are similar**.

We could add that one triangle is a 1·4 enlargement of the other, and we could mark pairs of equal angles as shown below:

VOLUMES OF SIMILAR SHAPES

These 2 soup cans are similar in shape. The smaller tin holds 290 g of soup. How much will the larger tin hold?

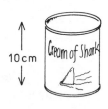

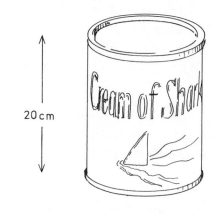

We can see that
lengths are in ratio $1:2$
so areas are in ratio $1^2:2^2=1:4$
and volumes are in ratio $1^3:2^3=1:8$.

So the larger tin holds 8 times as much. 8×290 g$=2\,320$ g, or **2·32 kg**.

Remember:	
For similar shapes	
Lengths in ratio	**a : b**
areas in ratio	**a² : b²**
volumes in ratio	**a³ : b³**

thinking hard !!

Example (difficult)

These 2 chocolate boxes are similar in shape and the larger holds 1 kg of chocolates.

The shaded triangles have areas as marked.

What weight of chocolates will the smaller box hold?

Let the sides be in ratio $a:b$.

From the picture, areas are in ratio
$54:150 = 9:25$ (cancelling)

So $a^2:b^2 = 9:25$
and so $a:b = 3:5$

This means that the volumes are in the ratio
$3^3:5^3 = 27:125$

Easy, wasn't it!

Hence volume of smaller box $= \dfrac{27}{125}$ of 1 kg = **216 g**.

CHAPTER 6—PROPORTION AND VARIATION

CONTENTS

DIRECT AND INVERSE PROPORTION

Direct: Susan is paid £16·80 for 7 hours work. What will she be paid for 2 hours work?

      7 hours   £16·80
      2 hours   £16·80÷7×2=£4·8

She will be paid **£4·80**.

Inverse: Last year it took 3 men 16 hours to weed a field, but this year 8 men have been employed to do the job. How long should it take?

      3 men   16 hours

      8 men $16 \times \frac{3}{8} = 6$

The job should take **6 hours**.

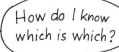

Notice this:

Direct:
As the hours increase,
the pay increases.

Inverse:
As the men increase,
the time **de**creases.

PIE CHARTS

The diagram shows the nutritional content of "Cracklie" cereal bars. If each bar weighs 40 g, how many grams of fibre does a bar contain?

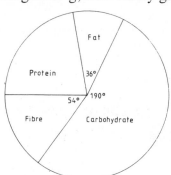

Fibre is represented by 54° (out of a total of 360°)

$$\text{weight of fibre} = \frac{54}{360} \text{ of } 40 \text{ g}$$

$$= \textbf{6 g.}$$

Example

Mark paid 5·3 francs for 1 litre of milk on holiday in France. Back in Scotland he paid 27p for 1 pint. Given that 1 pint is 0·569 litres and 10·4 francs made £1 at the time of his holiday, in which country was milk cheaper, France or Scotland?

One way to compare is to find the cost of a litre in sterling (British money) in each country:

France: 10·4 francs=£1

$$5.3 \text{ francs}= 1\times\frac{5.3}{10.4}=£0.5096$$

So 1 litre cost 51p in France.

Scotland: 1 pint=0·569 litre cost 27p

$$1 \text{ litre cost } 27p\times\frac{1}{0.569}=47.45p$$

So 1 litre cost 47p in Scotland.

The milk was cheaper in Scotland.

Don't just write the answer !!

The examiner wants to see what Maths you can do, and that means showing the working!

When you get a problem you find difficult, try substituting easy numbers and then see if you can do it. Then use the same method with the difficult numbers.

RATIO

Butter Icing
Beat together
100g icing sugar
50g butter

What should I use for 1·5 Kg Icing?

(a) The recipe shows that for 150 g of icing you need 100 g sugar and 50 g butter.

Ratio of sugar:butter is 100:50

or, more simply, 2:1.

Since 1·5 kg=1 500 g, split 1 500 g in the ratio 2:1 (total of 3 parts).

Divide 1 500 by 3 giving 500 g in each part.

Of sugar (2 parts) you need 1000 grams
Of butter (1 part) you need 500 grams.

(b) For chocolate icing 25 g cocoa should be added to the basic mixture. What is the ratio of sugar:butter:cocoa?

	sugar	:	butter	:	cocoa
	100 g	:	50 g	:	25 g
The ratio is:	4	:	2	:	1	(total of 7 parts)

(So 4/7 of the required weight of chocolate icing should be sugar, 2/7 butter and 1/7 cocoa.)

DIRECT VARIATION

Susan's pay is shown on this graph:

This is the graph of direct variation, a straight line through the origin.

Pay varies directly as number of hours.

(Pay ∝ number of hours)

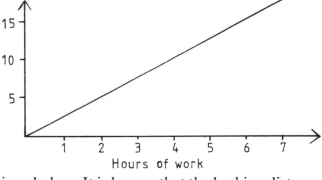

Example

A table of car braking distances is given below. It is known that the braking distance D varies directly as the square of the speed S. Draw a graph to show this is true and find a formula linking D and S.

Speed S (mph)	20	30	40	50	60	70
Braking distance (feet) D	20	45	80	125	180	245

You can draw the graph of D plotted against S for yourself.

Since the graph is not a straight line, D does not vary directly as S.

Calculate values of S^2 and make a new line in the table:

S^2	400	900	1600	2500	3600	4900
D	20	45	80	125	180	245

Now if you draw the graph of S^2 plotted against D you will get a straight line through the origin, and so:

Since D varies directly as S^2, D $\propto S^2$, so $D = kS^2$ for some constant k.

From the table or the graph we can see that D is always $S^2 \div 20$ (check it).

The formula linking D and S is: $\mathbf{D = \dfrac{S^2}{20}}$.

INVERSE VARIATION

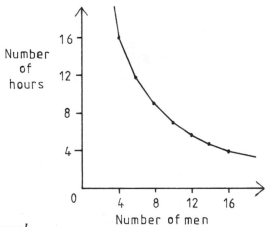

This graph shows the time taken to weed the field plotted against the number of men.

It is the graph of inverse variation.

T varies inversely as N,

$$\mathbf{T \propto \dfrac{1}{N}}.$$

Example

The time, T minutes, taken to cook pork in a microwave oven is inversely proportional to the power setting, P watts. It takes 4 minutes to cook a piece of pork on setting 600 watts. How long will it take to cook the pork on setting 800 watts?

$T \propto \dfrac{1}{P}$ so $T = \dfrac{k}{P}$

Substitute values and find k: $4 = \dfrac{k}{600} \Rightarrow k = 2400$.

The formula is $T = \dfrac{2400}{P}$ so if P = 800 watts, $T = \dfrac{2400}{800} = 3$ minutes.

It will take 3 minutes to cook the pork on 800 watts.

GRAPH OF $f(x) = \dfrac{a}{x}$

Compare the equation $T = \dfrac{k}{N}$ (example above) with $f(x) = \dfrac{a}{x}$.

k and a are both constants. We can see the similarity in the equations. The graphs too will be similar:

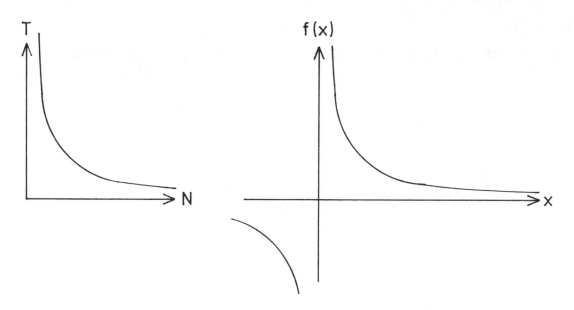

Try choosing a value for **a**, e.g. a=12, and plot points on the curve $y = \dfrac{a}{x}$,

remembering to take some negative values for x as well as positive values. Its shape will be similar to the graph above. You might like to try a negative value of **a** as well.

JOINT VARIATION

Example

The time taken for a box to slide down a delivery chute varies directly as the length of the chute and inversely as the square root of the difference in height of the top and bottom.

When the chute is 16 m long and the top is 4 m higher than the bottom the box takes 10 seconds to slide down the chute.

To reduce the risk of damage it is decided to lengthen the chute by 4 m. How long will it now take for the box to slide down the chute?

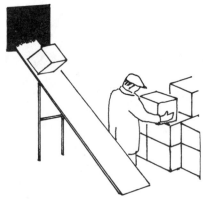

Symbols—L for length, T for time, H for height difference.

Pick out important information:

Time—varies directly as L and varies inversely as $\sqrt{H}$

So $T \propto \dfrac{L}{\sqrt{H}}$ or $T = \dfrac{kL}{\sqrt{H}}$

Substitute in values: $10 = \dfrac{k \times 16}{\sqrt{4}} \Rightarrow 16k = 20 \Rightarrow k = \dfrac{5}{4}$

Formula: $T = \dfrac{5L}{4\sqrt{H}}$ so $T = \dfrac{5 \times 20}{4\sqrt{4}} = 12 \cdot 5$

It now takes 12·5 seconds for the box to slide down the chute.

CHAPTER 7—TRIANGLES AND TRIGONOMETRY

CONTENTS

THE THEOREM OF PYTHAGORAS

The Theorem of Pythagoras is true for all right-angled triangles:

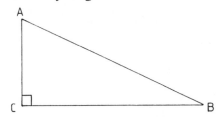

$$AB^2 = AC^2 + BC^2$$

(see page 42 for an example)

One use of this Theorem is to find the lengths of sloping lines on a grid:

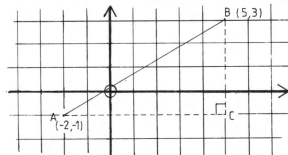

Find the length of AB:

By counting boxes we see that

AC=7 units and BC=4 units.

$AB^2 = AC^2 + BC^2$

$\quad\quad = 49 + 16 = 65$

so AB$=\sqrt{65}=$**8·1 units.**

TRIGONOMETRY IN RIGHT-ANGLED TRIANGLES

You must know which sides to use to find
sine, cosine or tangent of an angle.

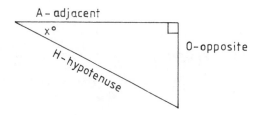

Learn!

$$\sin x = \frac{O}{H} \quad \cos x = \frac{A}{H} \quad \tan x = \frac{O}{A}$$

Of course you can remember
it any way you like, so long as
you do remember!

Your calculator must have ⌗sin⌗ ⌗cos⌗ and ⌗tan⌗ keys on it.

To find a trigonometric ratio, use ⌗sin⌗ ⌗cos⌗ and ⌗tan⌗ keys.

For example, cos 65°=0·423 (check this yourself).

To find an angle, use ⌗inv⌗ key, then ⌗sin⌗ ⌗cos⌗ or ⌗tan⌗

For example, if sin x°=0·312, then x=18·2°.

⌗inv⌗ might be ⌗2nd F⌗ on your calculator. Check that you know how to
use your own calculator for trigonometric calculations.

GRADIENT, ANGLES OF ELEVATION AND DEPRESSION

 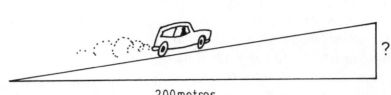

200 metres

The sign shows that this road climbs 1 metre vertically for every 10 metres horizontally. If this hill is 200 metres horizontally, then the car will have climbed one-tenth of that in height by the time it reaches the top, that is, 20 metres.

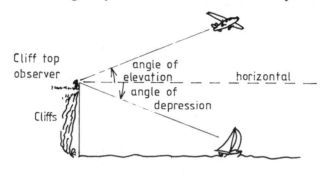

If the boat is 230 metres from the cliff-top observer, and the angle of depression is 40°, how far from the cliffs is the boat?

Draw a simplified diagram:

d stands for the distance we have to find.

$$\cos 40° = \frac{d}{230}$$

so d = 230 cos 40°

= 176

The boat is 176 metres from the cliffs.

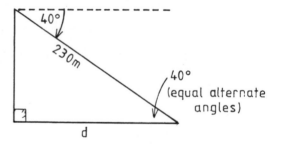

TRIGONOMETRIC FUNCTIONS AND THEIR GRAPHS

You should remember these graphs:

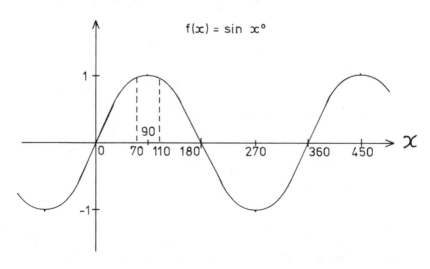

$f(x) = \sin x°$

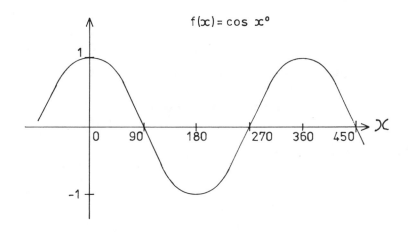

$$f(x) = \cos x°$$

The period of these functions is 360°.

From the symmetry we can see relationships between angles, for example,

sin 70°=sin 110°   (look at the graph to see this)

or, in general,   sin a°=sin (180−a)°   true for any value of a.

Also   sin 70°=−sin 250°

which in general is   sin a°=−sin (180+a)°

sin +ve	all +ve
(180−x)°	x°
(180+x)°	(360−x)°
tan +ve	cos +ve

There are other similar relationships for cosine and tangent. They can be seen from the graphs, or you may have been taught to remember them from the diagram opposite.

TRIGONOMETRIC EQUATIONS

As with any equations, we take terms containing the variable to the left.

For example, solve 2 sin x°+tan 35°=2   (x is the variable, 0⩽x<360)

$$2 \sin x° = 2 - \tan 35°$$
$$= 1.299 \ldots$$
$$\text{so } \sin x° = 0.649 \ldots$$
$$\text{and } x° = 40.5°.$$

Just a minute! Most trig. equations have more than one answer.

You will lose marks if you don't check that you have found *all* possible solutions!

From the graph of sin x°, we know that 40·5° and (180−40·5)° will have the same value for sine.

so sin x°=0·649

⇒ **x°=40·5° or 139·5°**.

Leave all your figures on the calculator during the working out—don't write down rounded-off figures and clear the screen in the middle of the calculation as it gives more chance for mistakes.

TRIGONOMETRIC IDENTITIES

> **You must know:**
>
> $$\tan x = \frac{\sin x}{\cos x} \quad \text{and} \quad \sin^2 x + \cos^2 x = 1$$
>
> **These are true for all values of x.**

Remember that $\sin^2 x$ is the way we write $(\sin x)^2$.

Example 1

Use algebra to show that the point (3cosa, 3sina) lies on the circle with equation $x^2 + y^2 = 9$.

Let x=3cosa   and   let y=3sina
$x^2 = 9\cos^2 a$ $y^2 = 9\sin^2 a$
$x^2 + y^2 = 9\,(\cos^2 a + \sin^2 a)$
$\Rightarrow x^2 + y^2 = 9$ since $\cos^2 a + \sin^2 a = 1$

(3cosa, 3sina) lies on the circle **since it satisfies the equation of the circle**.

Example 2

If $\sin A = \dfrac{7}{25}$, find the exact values of cos A and tan A, when $A \leqslant 90°$.

From $\sin^2 A + \cos^2 A = 1$, we get $\cos^2 A = 1 - \sin^2 A = 1 - \dfrac{49}{625} = \dfrac{576}{625}$

so $\cos A = \sqrt{\dfrac{576}{625}} = \dfrac{\mathbf{24}}{\mathbf{25}}$ disregard negative root since $A \leqslant 90°$.

$\tan A = \dfrac{\sin A}{\cos A} = \dfrac{7}{25} \div \dfrac{24}{25} = \dfrac{\mathbf{7}}{\mathbf{24}}.$

TRIGONOMETRY IN 3 DIMENSIONS

Example

Find the size of the angle between the space diagonal AG and the base of the cuboid opposite. (All lengths are in metres.)

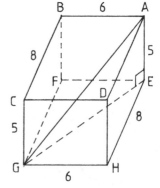

This sort of problem requires you to identify the correct angle before you use trigonometry.

The projection of AG on the base is the line EG.

So the required angle is $A\hat{G}E$.

Using The Theorem of Pythagoras in triangle HGE, we find EG=10m (check this).

Triangle AGE is right-angled at E (since AE is vertical and EG is horizontal).

So in triangle AGE, $\tan \hat{G} = \dfrac{5}{10} = 0{\cdot}5$

        which gives $\hat{G} = 27°$ to the nearest degree.

The angle between the space diagonal and the base is 27°.

$$\frac{a}{\sin A} = \frac{b}{\sin B} = \frac{c}{\sin C} \qquad \text{Sine rule}$$

$$a^2 = b^2 + c^2 - 2bc \cos A$$

or

$$\cos A = \frac{b^2 + c^2 - a^2}{2bc}$$ } Cosine rule

$$\text{Area} = \tfrac{1}{2}ab \sin C \qquad \text{Area formula}$$

Example

Two coastguard stations receive a distress signal from a ship at sea. From the first station B, the ship is on a bearing of 248° and from station C, which is 30 km south of B, the ship is on a bearing of 310°. How far is the ship from the nearer of the 2 coastguard stations?

From the given information the diagram opposite can be drawn.

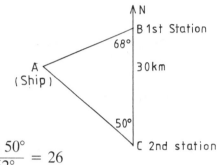

Calculate third angle: 62°

Since longest side is opposite largest angle, the first station is nearer.

Using sine rule, $\dfrac{30}{\sin 62°} = \dfrac{AB}{\sin 50°} \Rightarrow AB = \dfrac{30 \sin 50°}{\sin 62°} = 26$

It is 26 km to the second coastguard station.

Example 2

The area of triangle ABC is 20 cm^2. AB=8 cm and BC=6 cm. Investigate the size of angle B.

The area formula can be written Area $= \tfrac{1}{2}ac \sin B$

$$\text{so} \quad 20 = \tfrac{1}{2} \times 8 \times 6 \times \sin B$$

$$\sin B = \frac{20}{\tfrac{1}{2} \times 8 \times 6} = 0.833$$

hence **B = 56° or 124°.**

If you find the two answers puzzling, the sketch below shows why the base and height of the two triangles below are equal in length, and so, of course, have the same area.

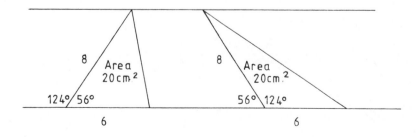

FAMILIES OF TRIGONOMETRIC CURVES

In these sketches different values of constant k have been chosen and the graphs drawn.

1. family $f(x) = \sin x° + k$

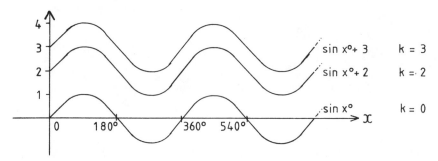

Adding k to sin x° moves the graph up or down (k units).

2. family $f(x) = \sin kx°$

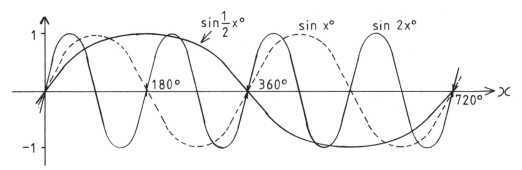

The period is altered: sin kx° will have k complete cycles in 360°.

3. family $f(x) = k \sin x°$

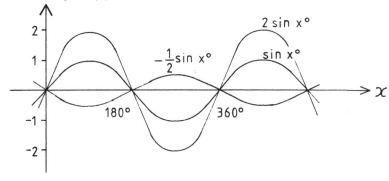

The amplitude is altered—it is k times as large.

4. family $f(x) = \sin (x+k)°$

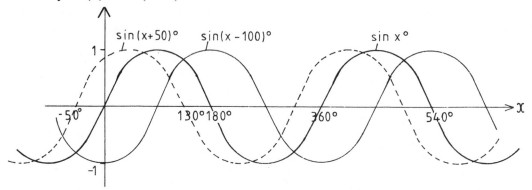

Adding a constant to x moves the graph along the x-axis, eg. sin(x+50)° is the graph of sin x° moved 50° to the left.

40

If the graph of sin x° is moved 90° to the left it will be the same as the graph of cos x°, that is, sin (x+90)°=cos x°.

You could draw some families of cosine curves for yourself, by putting cos x in place of sin x in the families above, choosing some values for k, and plotting the graphs.

Example

The graph below shows how the water level in a harbour rises and falls with the tide. The depth of water in the harbour has been plotted against the numbers of hours since midnight.

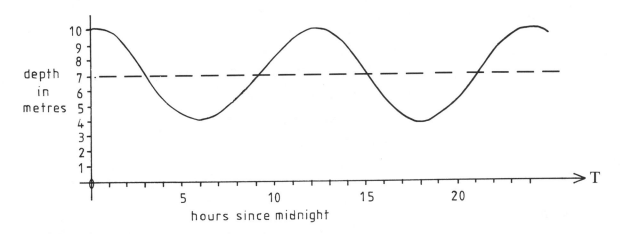

The equation of the graph can be written in the form:
$$f(T)=3 \cos (30T)°+A.$$

(a) Find the value of A.

So f(T)=3 cos (30T)°**+7.**

(b) A yacht is berthed in the harbour. It cannot leave until the water level rises above 8 metres. At what time after 0500 will it be able to leave the harbour?

The depth is 8 metres when
which means

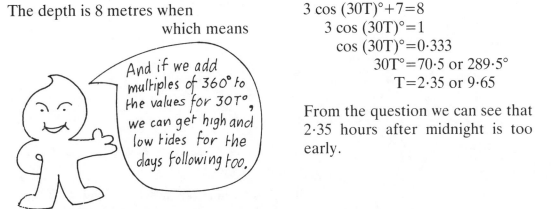

3 cos (30T)°+7=8
3 cos (30T)°=1
cos (30T)°=0·333
30T°=70·5 or 289·5°
T=2·35 or 9·65

From the question we can see that 2·35 hours after midnight is too early.

The yacht can leave 9·65 hours after midnight, which is **0939 hours.**

41

CONTENTS

CIRCUMFERENCE AND AREA

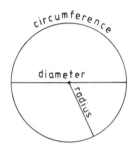

> **You must know:**
> **Circumference$=\pi\times$diameter**
> **($C=\pi d$ or $C=2\pi r$)**
> **Area$=\pi\times$square of radius**
> **($A=\pi r^2$)**
> **π is approx. 3·14**

Example

A cake, 20 cm in diameter, is to to iced on the top and have a decorative frill put round it. Find the area to be iced, and the length of the frill.

Radius is half the diameter, so r$=$10 cm.

The area to be iced is a circle.

Area$=\pi r^2=3\cdot14\times10\times10$

$\qquad=$**314 square centimetres.**

The frill goes around the circumference.

$C=\pi\times d=3\cdot14\times20$

$\qquad=$**62·8 cm.**

Always be sensible about rounding if you get an answer with many figures after the decimal point, which often happens when using π.

ANGLE IN A SEMICIRCLE

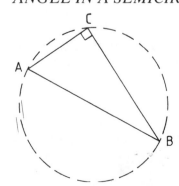

> **You must know:**
> **If AB is a diameter and C is a point on the circumference, then angle A$\hat{\text{C}}$B$=90°$.**

Remember, when you see the angle in a semicircle, you can use Pythagoras' Theorem or Trig.

Example

In the diagram on page 41 the circle has radius 5 cm and AC=6 cm. Find the length of BC and the size of angle B.

Using the Theorem of Pythagoras, $\qquad AC^2+BC^2=AB^2$
$$6^2+BC^2=10^2$$
so $\qquad BC^2=100-36=64$
and $\qquad$ **BC=8 cm**

Using trigonometry, $\qquad \tan A\hat{B}C=\dfrac{AC}{BC}=\dfrac{6}{8}=0{\cdot}75$

so $\qquad$ **A$\hat{B}$C=37°.**

TANGENTS

In the circle diagram opposite, TS is a tangent and OA is a radius which meets the tangent at A.

This means O$\hat{A}$T and O$\hat{A}$S are each 90°.

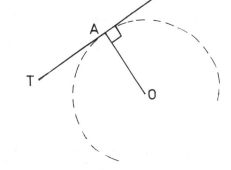

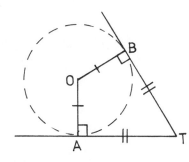

TA and TB are both tangents to the circle, so they are equal.

ARCS AND SECTORS

Drawing radii in a circle divides the circumference up into arcs and the area into sectors.

The ratios in which they are divided up will be the same and will depend on the ratio in which the angle at the centre is divided.

Here are some examples of equal ratios in the diagram opposite:

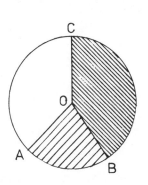

$$\frac{\text{size of A}\hat{O}\text{B}}{\text{size of B}\hat{O}\text{C}}=\frac{\text{length of arc AB}}{\text{length of arc BC}}=\frac{\text{area of sector AOB}}{\text{area of sector BOC}}$$

and $\dfrac{\text{size of A}\hat{O}\text{B}}{\text{size of A}\hat{O}\text{C}}=\dfrac{\text{length of arc AB}}{\text{length of arc AC}}$

Example

In the diagram on previous page angle AOB is 70° and arc AB is 4·3 cm. Find *(a)* the length of circumference of the circle; *(b)* the radius of the circle; and *(c)* the area of the sector AOB.

Write down suitable ratios:

(a) $\dfrac{\text{Circumference}}{4\cdot3\ \text{cm}}=\dfrac{360°}{70°}$

$C=\dfrac{360}{70}\times4\cdot3=\textbf{22·1 cm.}$

(b) But C=2πr, so $r=\dfrac{C}{2\pi}$

radius=**3·5 cm.**

(c) $\dfrac{\text{area of sector AOB}}{\text{area of circle}}=\dfrac{70°}{360°}$

area of sector AOB$=\dfrac{70}{360}\times\pi r^2$

=**7·5 square centimetres.**

CHORDS

In each of these diagrams OS is a radius and PQ is a chord of the circle.

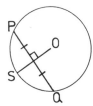

PQ is perpendicular to OS
and
OS bisects PQ.

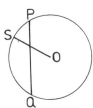

PQ is **not** perpendicular to OS
and
OS does **not** bisect PQ.

Example

The diameter of this oil tanker is 4 metres and the width of the oil surface is 3·2 metres. What reading will the dipstick give for the depth of oil in the tank?

CROSS-SECTION OF TANK

Since the oil surface AB is horizontal and the dipstick is vertical, they meet at right angles. The dipstick bisects the chord AB.

In the triangle, $x^2=2^2-1\cdot6^2$ which gives x=1·2 (check it).

The depth of oil is (2−1·2), so the **dipstick reading is 0·8 metres.**

44

SOME CALCULATIONS

This chapter contains 3 lists of calculations for you to try, one list on each of the next 3 pages. The first list is for the General papers, the next has calculations you will require for the early part of the Credit papers, and the third is for the more demanding questions in the Credit papers.

When you are working on a list, first cover over the second and third columns on the page—the working-out and answers—and look only at the questions. Work through the list doing everything you can. Then uncover the third column and check your answers. Use the second column to help you with those you get wrong or cannot do. You may need more practice in some of the skills—find a text-book with more examples if you do.

If you know your calculator well you will find many opportunities to use it and cut down the routine calculation work—and the time it takes. But be sure you do know what your calculator can do and how to do it! Not every calculator has a ⟨%⟩ key, for example, and not all will do calculations in scientific notation (standard form).

Scientific calculators may give you an answer in standard form if you enter a calculation which has a very large or small answer, but simpler calculators will give an error message instead. Check yours if you are not sure by doing something like $8\,000\,000 \times 3\,000\,000$.

Your calculator can only give approximate values for cos 45°, or $\sqrt{40}$. If the question asks for exact values then do not use your calculator!

Here are two examples to show you what that means:

Example 1
A square has an area of 20 cm². What is the length of its sides?
Length$=\sqrt{20}=$**4·47 cm** (No problem about using calculator here.)

Example 2
Express $\sqrt{20}$ as a surd in its simplest form.

4·47 is not a surd, and is only an approximation for $\sqrt{20}$, so we cannot use a calculator here.
But $20=2^2 \times 5$, so $\sqrt{20}=$**2$\sqrt{5}$**.

LIST 1 CALCULATION SKILLS FOR GENERAL EXAM

Remember to cover the second and third columns until you have tried working them out for yourself. (You may have a different method.)

Questions	Working out and hints	Answers
Simplify:		
1. $3(x-2y)$	multiply each term in bracket by 3	$3x-6y$
2. $6a-5a+2a$	this is rather like $6-5+2$, since all terms contain 'a'	$3a$
3. $(3x)^2$	means $3x$ times $3x$	$9x^2$
4. $2a+3b+5a$	collect 'a' terms and 'b' terms separately	$7a+3b$
5. $\left(\dfrac{1}{4}\right)^3$	$\dfrac{1}{4}\times\dfrac{1}{4}\times\dfrac{1}{4}$	$\dfrac{1}{64}$
6. 2^5	means $2\times2\times2\times2\times2$ (Don't add!)	32
7. $\sqrt{81}$	$81=9\times9$	9
Express:		
8. 17381 to the nearest hundred	We don't want the '81', but 81 is more than half of a hundred, so round up	17400
9. 3·8236 to 2 decimal places	We don't want the '36', and since 3 is less than 5, don't round up	3·82
10. 17·3 km in metres	$17\cdot3\times1000$	17300 metres
Calculate:		
11. $-2+6$	use a number line: start at -2, go up 6	4
12. $3+(-5)$	adding a negative means go **down** number line	-2
13. $1\frac{3}{4}+2\frac{1}{2}$	add whole numbers: 3 fractions—change to quarters—$\frac{3}{4}+\frac{1}{2}=\frac{3}{4}+\frac{2}{4}=\frac{5}{4}=1\frac{1}{4}$	$4\frac{1}{4}$
14. $\frac{4}{5}$ of 30 m	Find $\frac{1}{5}$ (divide by 5): 6 m $\frac{4}{5}$ is 4 times as much: 24 m	24 m
15. 15% of £56·95	$\dfrac{15}{100}\times56\cdot95=8\cdot5425$	£8·54 to nearest penny
Factorise:		
16. $2x+4y$	2 is common factor—put it outside brackets	$2(x+2y)$

LIST 2 CALCULATION SKILLS FOR CREDIT EXAM

You will need these skills to solve problems in the Credit examination. Cover up the second and third columns until you have tried working them out for yourself.

Questions	Working out and hints	Answers
Calculate:		
1. $-5-(-9)$	subtracting a negative is equivalent to adding: $-5+9$	4
2. $\dfrac{-24}{-6}$	numbers and signs separately, remember: $+ve \times -ve = -ve$ $-ve \times -ve = +ve$ (same for division)	4
3. $2\frac{1}{2} \div \frac{1}{3}$	$\dfrac{2\frac{1}{2} \times 3}{\frac{1}{3} \times 3} = \dfrac{7\frac{1}{2}}{1} = 7\frac{1}{2}$ (you may have a different method)	$7\frac{1}{2}$ or $7\cdot5$
Round to 3 significant figures:		
4. 60 082	The first non-zero digit is the first significant figure. Take it, and the	60 100
5. 0·00041635	next 2 figures. Decide whether you need to round up by looking at the next again figure. Fill in with zeros as required	0·000416
Expand:		
6. $3x(y+2x)$	Multiply each term in brackets by $3x$	$3xy+6x^2$
Factorise:		
7. a^2-b^2	difference of 2 squares	$(a-b)(a+b)$
8. $3x^2+5x$	'x' is common to both terms. Put it outside brackets	$x(3x+5)$
9. $x^2-3x-10$	Factorise first and last terms, then check middle term	$(x-5)(x+2)$
Simplify:		
10. $a^3 \cdot a^5$	to multiply powers of a, add indices	a^8
11. $\dfrac{a^6}{a^2}$	to divide, subtract indices	a^4
Express:		
12. £3·7 million in full	$3\cdot7 \times 1\,000\,000$	£3 700 000
13. £24·5 million in standard form	$24\cdot5 \times 1\,000\,000$ 24 500 000	£$(2\cdot45 \times 10^7)$

Remember to cover the second and third columns until you have tried them for yourself. (Your method might be different.)

Questions	Working out and hints	Answers
Simplify:		
1. $\sqrt{20}$	$\sqrt{2 \times 2 \times 5}$ (split into prime factors)	$2\sqrt{5}$
2. $(27)^{\frac{1}{3}}$	$(3 \times 3 \times 3)^{\frac{1}{3}}$	3
3. $3\sqrt{54}$	$3 \times \sqrt{2 \times 3 \times 3 \times 3} = 3 \times 3 \times \sqrt{2 \times 3}$	$9\sqrt{6}$
4. $\left(\dfrac{9}{16}\right)^{\frac{1}{2}}$	$= \dfrac{9^{\frac{1}{2}}}{16^{\frac{1}{2}}} = \dfrac{3}{4}$	$\dfrac{3}{4}$
5. $5\sqrt{2} - 2\sqrt{2}$	compare with $5a - 2a$	$3\sqrt{2}$
6. $\dfrac{10a^2 - 3ab - b^2}{15a + 3b}$	*factorise:* $\dfrac{(5a+b)(2a-b)}{3(5a+b)}$	$\dfrac{2a-b}{3}$
7. $\dfrac{5-2x}{3} - \dfrac{8x-3}{2x+1}$	$\dfrac{(5-2x)(2x+1)}{3(2x+1)} - \dfrac{3(8x-3)}{3(2x+1)}$ $= \dfrac{10x+5-4x^2-2x-24x+9}{3(2x+1)}$	$\dfrac{14-16x-4x^2}{3(2x+1)}$
8. $(a^2)^3$	$a^{2 \times 3}$ To raise to a power, multiply indices	a^6
9. $\dfrac{y^5}{y^{-2}}$	$y^{-2} = \dfrac{1}{y^2}$ so $\dfrac{1}{y^{-2}} = y^2$ $\dfrac{y^5}{y^{-2}} = y^5 \times y^2 = y^7$	y^7
10. $3a^{-\frac{1}{2}}(a^{\frac{1}{2}} + a^{-\frac{3}{2}})$	$3a^{-\frac{1}{2}} \times a^{\frac{1}{2}} = 3a^0 = 3$ $3a^{-\frac{1}{2}} \times a^{-\frac{3}{2}} = 3a^{-2}$	$3 + 3a^{-2}$
Factorise:		
11. $4a^2 - 25b^2$	$(2a)^2 - (5b)^2$ difference of squares	$(2a-5b)(2a+5b)$
Express with rational denominator:		
12. $\dfrac{3}{\sqrt{20}}$	$\dfrac{3}{\sqrt{5 \times 4}} = \dfrac{3}{2\sqrt{5}} \times \dfrac{\sqrt{5}}{\sqrt{5}} = \dfrac{3\sqrt{5}}{2 \times 5}$	$\dfrac{3\sqrt{5}}{10}$